Scholastic's

# The Magic School Bus

™

## PLANTS SEEDS
### A Book About How Living Things Grow

Hippo

**From an episode of the animated TV series
produced by Scholastic Productions, Inc.
Based on *The Magic School Bus* books
written by Joanna Cole and illustrated by Bruce Degen.**

*TV tie-in book by Linda Ward Beech
and illustrated by Joel Schick.
TV script written by John May,
Kristin Laskas Martin, and Jocelyn Stevenson.*

Scholastic Children's Books,
7-9 Pratt Street, London NW1 OAE UK
A division of Scholastic Limited
London ~ New York ~ Toronto ~ Sydney ~ Auckland

First published by Scholastic Inc. 1995
This edition published in the UK by Scholastic Limited 1996

ISBN: 0 590 13632 1

Typeset by Rapid Reprographics
Printed in Italy by Amadeus S.p.A. - Rome

10 9 8 7 6 5 4 3 2 1

Every class probably learns about plants and seeds.
But not every class has Miss Frizzle for a teacher.

When Miss Frizzle does something, she does it properly. She started by letting us plant a whole garden behind our school.

A photographer was coming
to take a picture of our garden,
so we all wanted it to look its best.

"To think that these beautiful tomato plants started from tiny seeds," Carlos said. "Add some soil, sunshine, water, and some tender, loving care, and you've got this great garden."

"And once that photographer takes our picture, we'll be famous!" Carlos said. "We could be on the cover of *Plant It!* magazine! Would you like me to autograph your seed packet, Dorothy Ann?"

"I'll think about it!" said Dorothy Ann.

Phoebe was not as excited as Carlos. "I wish I had the beautiful plant I grew at my old school."

Tim put the finishing touch on a drawing.

Phoebe smiled. "That's it!  Thank you, Tim," she said. "Still, I wish I had the real thing for our picture this afternoon."

Miss Frizzle saw the drawing. "Your plant looks lovely, Phoebe," she said. "Don't worry! We can easily stop at your old school on a little field trip!"

We all piled onto the old school bus. Carlos was worried that we might not get back in time for the photographer.

"This could take all day! Couldn't we fly or something, Miss Frizzle?"

"Excellent idea, Carlos!" she said. Suddenly the whole bus began to spin. It rose in the air as if it had wings. It did have wings! We were riding in a ladybird!

As we flew over buildings and trees, Phoebe began to look nervous. "What if Mr Seedplot sees us?" she asked. "We never turned into ladybirds when *he* was my teacher."

Just then, we all saw a school below. Phoebe stared. "There it is!" she gasped.

The bus swooped in low through the school's garden. It looked like a jungle. "Here's the perfect landing pad – I mean petal," said Miss Frizzle. The bus landed with a bounce and crawled along the petal of a huge flower.

This is one of my plants!

We crawled one step too far. Suddenly, our ladybird bus slid into something wet and slippery.

"We're stuck in some goop!" Ralphie yelled.

"It's called nectar," Dorothy Ann said.

"Follow me, class!" said the Friz. She opened the doors and slipped out into the lake of nectar.

We didn't know it then, but Mr Seedplot could have reached out and picked us. "Phoebe's plants certainly have grown well," he said to himself. "She worked hard on them. I really should take one to her new school for her."

Mr Seedplot heard a buzz and looked up. "Ah, bees! I won't disturb their work now," he said, turning to a patch of tomato plants.

We also saw the bees coming...and they were heading right into our flower.

"Yikes!  Air raid!" shouted Arnold.

"Glory bee!" said the Friz happily. "As soon as these bees drink enough nectar, then we can crawl out of here. All aboard the ladybus, please. Next stop, anther!"

Dorothy Ann is amazing. Even upside down, she could remember what she had read that morning. "The *anther* is the part of the flower that makes pollen," she said.

These yellow balls are pollen? Pollen makes me... ah...ah... CHOO! ...sneeze.

There we were, on top of the anther, with bees buzzing all around us.

It was then that Phoebe caught sight of her old teacher. "It's Mr Seedplot!" she yelled. "He'll see us!  Do something!  Quickly!"

Miss Frizzle stayed calm. "No problem," she said cheerfully. "We'll get out of here the same way the pollen does."

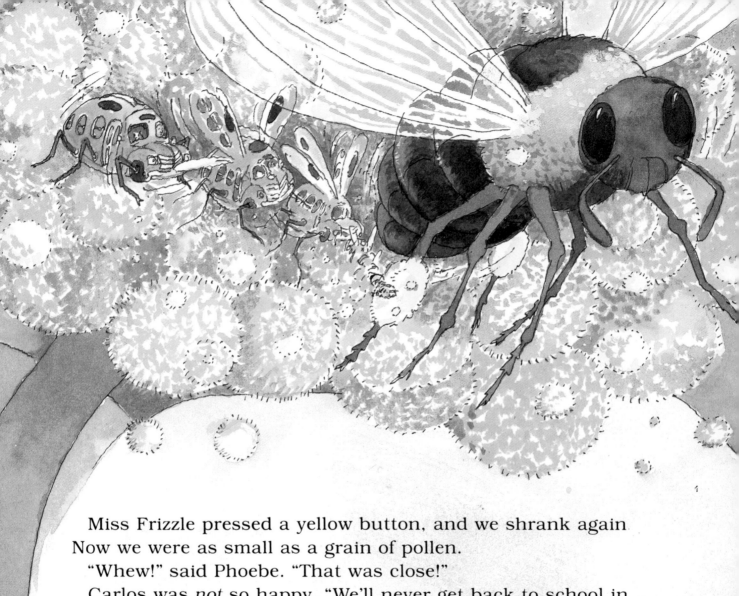

Miss Frizzle pressed a yellow button, and we shrank again. Now we were as small as a grain of pollen.

"Whew!" said Phoebe. "That was close!"

Carlos was *not* so happy. "We'll never get back to school in time for the photographer," he grumbled.

"*Bee* of good cheer. We're on our way," said Miss Frizzle.

"Hang on!" she called as the leg of a passing bee swept us up and away.

At my old school,
we never rode on bees.

We ARE at
your old school,
Phoebe.

Off we flew, stuck to the leg of that bee. It was a short ride. At the very next plant, the bee bumped a flower and brushed us off, along with a lot of pollen.

"Here we are!" Miss Frizzle announced.

"*Where?*" Phoebe asked.

Tim showed her his picture. "I think we're on this centre part – the *stigma*," Tim said.

The bee had dropped a lot of pollen here. With a big sneeze, Arnold bumped into the grain of pollen, knocked it over... and fell down some kind of tunnel underneath!

Arnold found a pollen tube!

Ah-choo!

Phoebe looked down the tube. "Mr Seedplot will never spot us down there!" she said, and she hopped into the tube and slid down.

Miss Frizzle beamed. "That's the spirit! Take chances! Make mistakes! Check out pollen tubes! Yahoo!" she yelled as she, too, jumped down the tube.

We all slid to the bottom of the pollen tube.

"*Now* where are we?" asked Carlos. "Couldn't we just grab one of Phoebe's plants and go back to school?"

"I don't think we need a whole plant," Keesha said. "Look at this!" She pointed to something that looked like a big rock. "It's a seed!"

"I get it!" Dorothy Ann said. "When pollen from one flower lands on the stigma of another, it grows a pollen tube, finds one of these egg cells, and together they make a seed!"

Carlos still wasn't happy. "No seed can grow into a plant by three o'clock," he said.

"Not without some help," said Miss Frizzle. She reached into the bus and pressed a button...and suddenly things went wild. The seeds were growing bigger and sprouting hair!

"We need to hurry things along a bit," said Miss Frizzle.
"Everyone on the bus, please!"

We all rushed back to the bus, the doors slammed shut,
and we drove up and on to one of the biggest seeds.

As the seeds around us grew bigger, the flower burst open.
We felt the sun shine in and a breeze blowing through the
windows of the bus. Suddenly our seed flew into the air – with
us on board.

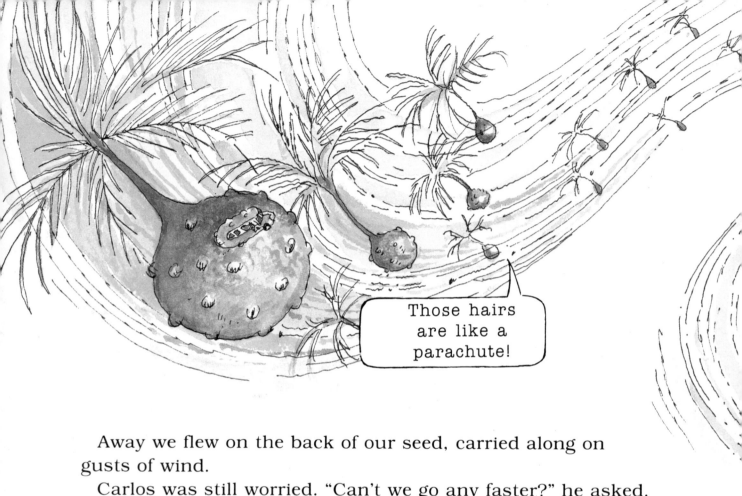

Those hairs are like a parachute!

Away we flew on the back of our seed, carried along on gusts of wind.

Carlos was still worried. "Can't we go any faster?" he asked.

"Well," Miss Frizzle said, "this is pretty fast for a seed. But there are seeds that travel by attaching themselves to dogs or birds...or people," she said, eyeing a man on a bicycle.

"*No!*" croaked Phoebe. "That's Mr Seedplot's hair. "Oh, how embarrassing!" Phoebe groaned.

Was someone
calling me?

We were almost home, still stuck in Mr Seedplot's hair, and
we hadn't even been introduced. So we all shouted, "Hello,
Mr Seedplot!" – except for Phoebe, who was too embarrassed to talk.

But when Mr Seedplot swung his head to see who
was calling him, we flew off.

"Last stop!" Miss Frizzle announced. She pushed a button.
*Poof!* The bus got big again. She pushed another button. *Poof!*
The seed, which had landed in our garden, grew into a tall
plant with beautiful flowers.

"Ah, there you are!" Mr Seedplot said when he spotted us. "I brought one of Phoebe's plants, but I see that she already has one. Nice to see you again, Miss Frizzle."

Phoebe gasped. "You mean you've met Miss Frizzle before?" she said.

Mr Seedplot smiled. "Yes. She's a very special person."

PLANT IT!

The Magic
of Gardening

We had to agree. Miss Frizzle is special, all right!

## Letter to the Editor of *Plant It!* magazine

Dear Editor,

I liked the pictures of the garden planted by Miss Frizzle's class. But there are a few things I'd like to point out to you about your article.

- First of all, I have never heard of a school bus that could turn into a ladybird or a grain of pollen.
- Second, I don't see how anyone could be allergic to such a big grain of pollen. It could never get inside your nose!
- Also, I would like to know how anyone could make a seed or plant grow in just a few seconds. Even with my secret home-made fertiliser recipe, my plants take a long time to grow and to make seeds – days, weeks, or even months!
- In fact, I don't think I've ever seen a plant quite like Phoebe's. Did you invent that plant?
- And you must have done some kind of trick photography on Miss Frizzle's clothes, because *no one* dresses like that.

Your faithful reader
D. Tractor

Dear Reader,

You are absolutely right. Could you send us your fertiliser recipe?

The Editor

# A Note to Parents, Teachers and Kids

A seed is a tiny plant in a wonderfully efficient package, ready to grow when conditions are right. This book tells the story of seeds and the flowers that make them.

• Pollen is manufactured by the anther, the top part of a flower's stamen. This is the male part of the flower.

• The colours, markings, and scents of flowers attract animals such as bees and hummingbirds, which drink the flower's nectar and carry its pollen to other flowers. Pollen may also travel on the wind (as with grasses and many trees) or water (as with pond weed).

• When pollen lands on the stigma of its own kind of flower, it grows a pollen tube that reaches down the pistil to the ovary, the female part of the flower. A sperm cell from the pollen travels down the tube and joins with an egg cell. The fertilised egg cell begins to divide and becomes a seed.

• Seeds travel in many ways: on the wind, by attaching themselves to animals or to people's clothing, in the digestive systems of animals, or by bursting forcefully from a pod or fruit.

Children can enjoy their own plant adventure by looking for these parts on different kinds of flowers, and by planting seeds themselves.

*Miss Frizzle*